Mrs May made a dragon. The children helped her.

Mrs May painted the head.

The children painted the body.

The dragon had a long body. The
children liked the dragon.

They wanted to do the dragon
dance.

The children got inside the body. Mrs May helped them.

"It's made of paper,"
said Mrs May. "Be careful."

Anneena was inside the head.

"Be careful," said Mrs May. "Don't tear the paper."

The mums and dads came.

The children did the dragon dance.
"What a good dragon," said
everyone.

Oh no! The dragon dance went wrong.

The dragon tore in half.

The children were upset.

"Never mind," said Mrs May. "It was only made of paper."

Anneena's mum had an idea. She told the mums and dads.

"What a good idea," they said.

The mums and dads made a
dragon. They made a long body.

They made a big head.

The dragon looked wonderful.

The children were pleased. They
wanted to do the dragon dance.

The children went into town. They
did the dragon dance.

"Come to the school fair,"
said Chip.

"What a lot of people," said
Mrs May. "Thanks to the
dragon."